Peter Pan

Based on the original story
by James M. Barrie

Retold by Andrea Stacy Leach

Illustrated by Denny Bond

Allan Publishers, Inc.

Wendy, John, and
Michael Darling lived in London. One
night, Wendy woke to find a strange boy sitting on the floor, crying.

"My name is Wendy," she said. "Who are you? Why are you crying?"

"I'm Peter Pan," the boy replied. "I'm crying because my shadow
won't stick to me."

"Don't cry," Wendy said. "We can fix that." And she sewed Peter's
shadow to the tips of his shoes. Peter was delighted.

"Fly back to Neverland with me and my fairy, Tinker Bell," Peter
begged. "You could be our mother and take care of us."

"Can you teach me to fly?" Wendy asked. Peter nodded.

"Let's wake John and Michael," Wendy said. "You can teach us all
to fly and then we will leave for Neverland!"

The children were soon flying around the room. Then—Swoosh!
Out the window they all flew.

Wendy, John, and Michael flew behind Peter Pan and Tinker Bell, following the golden arrows that pointed the way to Neverland. Finally, they were flying over the island.

"The lost boys live with me and Tinker Bell. I'm their captain," Peter said. "The Indians live over there, and the mermaids live in the lagoon. And there are pirates too, led by Captain Hook."

"Pirates?" exclaimed Wendy, John, and Michael, all in the same breath. Wendy was frightened, but Michael and John wanted to see the pirates right away.

"Hook's the meanest pirate ever," Peter warned.
"But he's afraid of the crocodile. The crocodile
bit off Hook's hand and liked the taste so much
that it follows him, hoping for more. Luckily
for Hook, the crocodile swallowed a
clock. It goes 'Tick, Tock,' and warns
Hook when the crocodile is nearby."

"Oh, my," cried Wendy, not sure if she really
wanted to stay in Neverland after all.

Peter led Wendy, John, and Michael to his house under the woods. They entered through a door hidden in an old tree stump. When the lost boys saw Wendy, they shouted, "Hooray! Will you be our mother?"

"I'm only a little girl," Wendy answered. "I have no experience." But the lost boys looked so sad that she said, "I'll do my best."

That night Wendy tucked the boys into bed and told them the tale of Cinderella.

Life was pleasant in the cozy house under the woods. Wendy took care of the boys, who explored the island during the day. At night, they gathered for meals, played make-believe games, and listened while Wendy told them stories.

One day, Peter and the children went exploring near the mermaids' lagoon. Suddenly Peter yelled, "Pirates! Take cover." The boys ran away, and Peter and Wendy hid.

Peter and Wendy could see that the pirates had tied up Tiger Lily, the Indian princess. The pirates had left her on a rock in the lagoon. Peter was afraid that Tiger Lily would drown when the tide came in. He had to save her! In a voice that sounded just like Captain Hook's, he shouted, "Set her free!"

"But, Captain," the pirates yelled, "you ordered us to bring her here!"

"Let her go!" Peter roared, still sounding like Hook.

"Aye, aye," the pirates said, and set Tiger Lily free. She swam quickly back to the Indian camp.

When Captain Hook found out what had happened, he knew Peter had tricked his pirates. Hook was furious!

That night, Wendy told the boys a story about three children who left their parents and flew to Neverland. Their mother and father missed them very much. The children loved Neverland, but they never forgot their home.

"Did they ever go back?" the lost boys asked.

"Oh, yes," Wendy replied. "They flew home to their mommy and daddy, and everyone was happy."

The story made Wendy, John, and Michael homesick. They decided to fly home the next morning. "If you come back with us," Wendy told the lost boys, "I'm sure our mother and father would adopt you."

"Hooray!" shouted the boys, jumping with joy.

Wendy asked Peter if he and Tinker Bell would come home with them too. But Peter didn't want to live where grown-ups could tell him what to do.

Peter was sad that his friends were leaving. Still, he wanted the children to arrive home safely, so he asked Tinker Bell to guide them on their trip.

Early the next morning, Tinker Bell and the children left the house under the woods. But Captain Hook's pirates were hiding nearby. They captured all the children, tied them up, and marched them towards the pirate ship.

Tinker Bell escaped, and hurried back to tell Peter what had happened.

"It's Hook or me this time!" yelled Peter to Tinker Bell as they flew off to save Wendy and the boys.

On the pirate ship, Captain Hook demanded, "Who wants to become a pirate?" The boys shook their heads.

"Then make them walk the plank!" Hook roared. The boys tried to look brave, but they were afraid.

Suddenly, they heard the "Tick, Tock" of the crocodile. Now it was Captain Hook's turn to be afraid.

But the "Tick, Tock" was only Peter, imitating the crocodile. He flew onto the deck and shouted, "I've got you now, Hook!"

Captain Hook jumped up and swung at Peter with his sword. Peter was quick, and stepped away. He slashed at Hook with his own sword until they came close to the edge of the ship.

Peter lunged with his sword, and Hook fell into the sea, where the crocodile was waiting for him. And that was the end of Captain Hook!

When Peter was certain that Hook was gone forever, he and Tinker Bell set off for London with Wendy and the boys.

Wendy's parents were happy to see their children again. Mr. and Mrs. Darling hugged Wendy, John, and Michael, and agreed to adopt the lost boys. They asked Peter to stay also, but he said, "I'm going to stay in Neverland where I never have to grow up."

"Goodbye then, Peter. We'll miss you," everyone called. Peter Pan and Tinker Bell waved goodbye and flew home to Neverland.